The Cliffs of
Hartland Quay

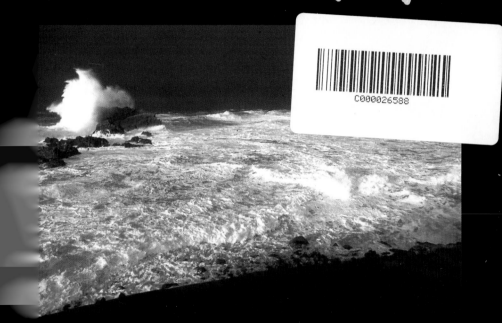

C000026588

alking down the path beyond 'The Street' towards Warren Beach for the first ne, most people will pause above the beach, in awe at the sheer scale and ajesty of the massive cliffs across the bay and will sense the power of the ow heaving Atlantic rollers which, on most days, pulse into the bay to thrust the beach or burst against the dark, fringing saw-tooth rocks.

his guide assumes that this sense of wonder can be enhanced by an nderstanding of how such a landscape came about. To appreciate the ature of this astonishing coast fully you need to walk the cliffs but even if his is not possible, I hope that this booklet enables you to wander at least in our imagination and to enjoy the story of this remarkable landscape.

Peter Keene 1st February 2006

bove: *Life Rock, Warren Beach in evening sunlight after a storm.*
over: *From St Catherine's Tor looking south (Paul Lewin)*

The Hartland Heritage Coast

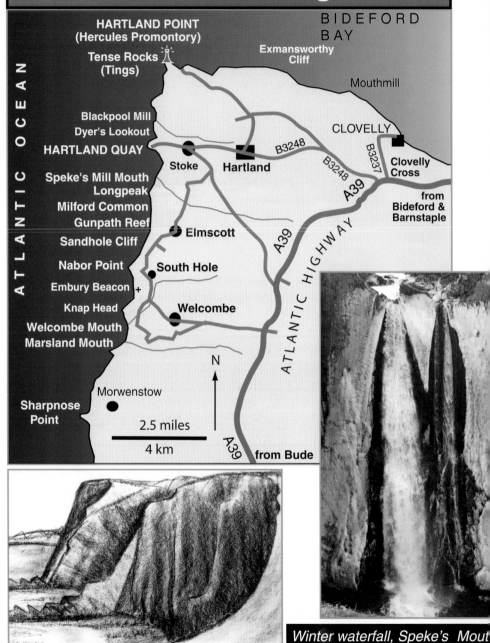

HARTLAND POINT
(Hercules Promontory)

BIDEFORD BAY

Exmansworthy Cliff

Tense Rocks (Tings)

Mouthmill

ATLANTIC OCEAN

Blackpool Mill
Dyer's Lookout
HARTLAND QUAY

Stoke   Hartland

CLOVELLY

B3248

B3248

B3237

Clovelly Cross

Speke's Mill Mouth
Longpeak
Milford Common
Gunpath Reef

Sandhole Cliff

Nabor Point

Embury Beacon +

Knap Head

Welcombe Mouth
Marsland Mouth

Elmscott

South Hole

Welcombe

from Bideford & Barnstaple

A39

ATLANTIC HIGHWAY

N

Sharpnose Point

Morwenstow

2.5 miles

4 km

A39

from Bude

*Winter waterfall, Speke's Mout
Atlantic Cliffs (Jo Keene)*

A proposed cliff walk

The proposed walk of about two miles has a straightforward commentary which is best described as a 'landscape companion'. This draws attention to wide-ranging points of interest in the landscape. There are pleasant spots for a picnic both on the cliff tops or on the beach at Speke's Mill Mouth. You can also extend the walk by following the coastal path to the south beyond the spectacular coastal waterfall at Speke's Mill Mouth (see left).

DIRECTIONS for moving between viewpoints are printed in yellow panels. Use these in conjunction with the map on the rear cover.

ⓘ Information and explanation

One way of enhancing the enjoyment of this walk is to try 'reading the landscape', considering the possible evolution or history of whatever, in the scenery, seems to call for some explanation or comment. For those who become sufficiently absorbed by what they find and seek further information or interpretation, the panels flagged in green, offer a more detailed commentary on this scenery. Refer to these as you wish. Some key words for reading the landscape are printed in *italics,* and are recalled on pages 44 and 45.

Literary quotes are presented within blue tinted boxes with most sources listed on page 48.

A Starting the walk at Warren Beach

The starting point is viewpoint (A) overlooking Warren Beach. From the lowest car park, walk north along 'The Street'. To your left are toilets, a shop and the 'Shipwreck Museum'. To the right is the 'Wreckers Retreat' and the Hotel.

Beyond 'The Street', the track descends towards Warren Beach. Pause at the top of the slipway to absorb the view. Then, if you are so inclined, find somewhere comfortable nearby where you can read the introduction to this view.

ROCK and SEA dominate this scene. Here, at its simplest and most dramatic, we witness both what rock has created and what sea has pulled asunder. Both contribute to this panorama and it is fitting to reflect on how each has played its role in this visible cycle of construction and destruction.

The Rocks: the power of the earth

The story of the rocks of the Hartland Coast could be said to begin over 300 million years ago when, what was to be the north-west coast of Devon, was the floor of an isolated arm of a great ocean sitting astride the equator. On a relatively flat sea floor, were deposited alternating layers of fine sand and mud. As they became deeply buried beneath subsequent layers these soft sediments were gradually compressed, until eventually they became the alternating beds of pale sandstones and darker mudstones which make up the rocks of Hartland Quay.

Some 300 million years ago, in 'Carboniferous' times, the peace of this ocean basin was disturbed by the approach of two super-continents which, at that time lay south of the equator. One continent called EURUSSIA was travelling slowly north and the other, called GONDWANA, was travelling rapidly north. The inevitable collision of these two huge land masses crumpled and compressed the thick layers of sea-floor sediments trapped between, creating a broad mountain system comparable in size to the Alps today. The near-horizontal beds of the former ocean floor were contorted into the upfolds and downfolds, examples of which can be seen in Warren Cliff. The compression, folding and fracturing occurred deep within the mountain chain, some 5-8km below the Carboniferous land surface.

However, although the layers of pale sandstone and dark mudstones are easy to recognise both on the shore and in the face of Warren Cliff, these beds are clearly no longer horizontal. So what happened?

4

1

super-continent

EURUSSIA

Including
North Europe,
Northern Asia and
North America

How much were these sediments compressed? The sheer weight of overlying sediments squeezed out water present in the beds and compacted them until they were a fraction of their original thickness but they have also been compressed laterally. Look again at the face of Warren Cliff. Notice how individual beds swing up and down across the cliff face.

Try choosing a clear, well-defined bed and follow its path over the cliff-face. Does your example match the contortions of the bed highlighted in white on the photo above?

super-continent

GONDWANA

Including Southern
Europe, Africa,
South America,
Australia and
Antarctica

From north (left) to south (right), horizontally this photograph covers about 300 metres (1000 feet) of cliff face. The selected white bed, measured along its length over the same horizontal distance, is 600 metres (2000 feet) long. If we assume we are viewing the cliff at right angles to the direction of compression, it suggests that here, 600 metres of equatorial sea bed was compressed within the earth's crust to half its former length.

Pressure in the earth's crust may produce folding but when pressure is released rapidly, the rock may crack or fracture. If the rocks on one side of the fracture move relative to the rock sequence on the other side then a fault is created. Can you see any evidence of this?

ⓘ A folded landscape

Wherever bare rock is exposed, either in the cliffs or rocky shore, the folded structure is evident. Even where the crest or trough of a fold is not visible, limbs of steeply tilted sandstone sheets signal the hidden or eroded fold. In fact, the rocks have folded in a surprising number of different ways. Look towards the left (north) end of Warren Beach. Here a particularly thick bed of sandstone forms a gentle open fold roofing a wide sea cave (top right), penetrating a surprising way into the cliff (bottom right).

In contrast (left), the spectacular contorted folding at Embury Beach, beneath Embury Beacon, some 3.5 miles (6km) south of Hartland Quay (see page 2) was helped by the presence of rapidly alternating thin beds of pale sandstone and dark carbon-rich mudstones.

6

It was noted (page 4) that the whole district was once folded, fractured and squeezed into a high mountain chain. Yet, these Alp-like mountains which once covered Devon and Cornwall are today nowhere to be seen? Where have they gone?

It's really just a matter of getting your mind around the timescale involved. The Alps and Himalayas are merely 50 million years old. The continental collision which created the Variscan mountains of Devon and Cornwall happened some 290 million years ago. Ample time, then, for rivers, slope movements or any other erosional process to reduce these mountain ranges to their roots, creating a rock plane, an 'erosional surface', so gentle that, lacking the energy provided by gradient, erosional processes were unable, at the time it was formed to continue any effective down-cutting below this base level.

Can you identify any *erosional surface* in this landscape? Look at the top of Warren Cliff. Just below soil level is a rock plane which cuts straight across folded beds, as if with a knife. This is 'an *erosional surface*'. Such surfaces, often termed *plateaux*, are common in Devon and Cornwall.

These *plateaux* are a very distinctive feature of the landscape. Yet, travelling by car across the plateaux of North Devon you can be completely unaware of the intense rock folding beneath your feet.

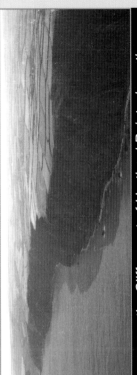

Exmansworthy Cliffs, east of Hartland Point where the coastal plateau is about 130 metres high.

If the day is clear, look towards Lundy on the horizon to the north, some 12 miles off Hartland Point. Here, an erosional surface has sliced straight across a mass of hard granite. This Eocene granite originally solidified deep underground some 50 million years ago, so this erosion surface must be younger than that.

7

The Sea: the power of the waves

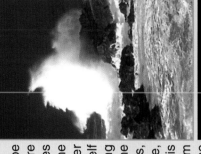

Storm wave breaks on Life Rock,

Making Waves

Most waves (although not tsunami) are created by winds blowing over and agitating the water surface. The stronger the winds and the longer they blow, the more powerful and higher will be the waves and the greater the energy that is transferred from the wind to the sea. Once formed, perhaps in a distant Atlantic storm, these waves, will spread out from their source. A day or so later, having lost little of their energy, they will arrive at Hartland Quay.

"Where on Hartland's tempest-furrowed shore Breaks the long swell from farthest Labrador."

Such swell waves are characterised by their regular wavelength with crests which, in deep water, are smooth and unbroken. When they reach shallow water they become unstable and collapse into lines of breakers. These swell waves are loved by surfers. Even on windless days, lines of Atlantic rollers can still be seen pulsing into the bay. Local gales, on the other hand, produce a chaotic violent sea of wind-forced waves, without long crests, they peak and chop in all directions. A very difficult sea to handle near rocks.

Waves and erosion

The force of an Atlantic wave can be as much as 30 tonnes per square metre. When such a wave smashes against a sea wall, you can feel the awesome shudder of its power beneath you. Although water itself cannot be compressed, breaking waves can trap air in cracks in the rock face and, as the wave recedes, the air, trapped under great pressure, will *'explosively decompress'*. This can physically blow fragments from the rock face which contributes to the debris on the beach.

The presence of beach debris is also important as it provides the breaking wave with tools with which to batter the solid rock (*abrasion*) and to grind beach debris in the wave-mill into smaller pieces (*attrition*). Waves are thus very effective *agents of erosion* particularly at the cliff foot. However, on the sea bed, just a few metres below the waves, the sea is normally relatively quiescent, even in a storm. Vigorous wave erosion is therefore limited to a narrow zone between low and high tide.

8

ⓘ How waves carved Warren Cliff

We know that the rocks of which Warren Cliff are composed were formed over 300,000,000 years ago but they have only been exposed as sea cliffs within the last 3000 years, in a sequence of events which was repeated around our shores in many places. The story goes something like this:

1 Some 18,000 years ago during the most severe cold stage of the last ice age (table on page 46), world sea level was about 120 metres lower than today. A tundra landscape stretched from here to Wales. Warren Cliff and the Bristol Channel did not exist.

2 However, towards the end of the ice age, as the world got warmer, so sea level rose, first rapidly flooding the dry English and Bristol Channels and then gradually slowing down until, about 3000 years ago, sea level became relatively stable at a height approaching that of the sea today.

3 If we try to reconstruct the coastal scenery of Hartland Quay at that time we must imagine the sea lapping against a sloping wooded coastal hillside, without sea cliffs. When the sea arrived, 3000 years ago, the coastline would have looked like this.

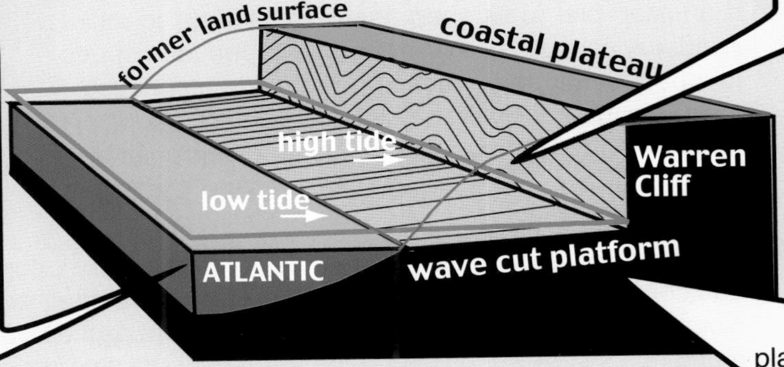

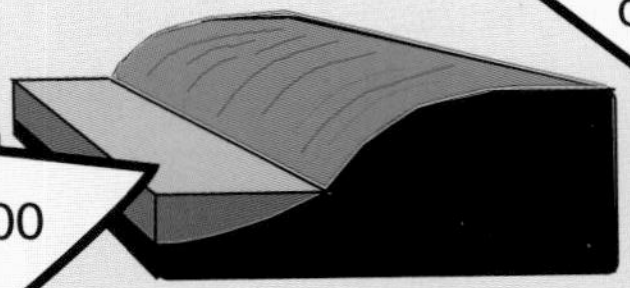

4 Between high and low water, waves begin to cut a rock-shelf (a *wave-cut platform*) which gets wider as time passes.

This platform is the plane below which further downward erosion by waves is ineffective. It slopes gently seawards slicing straight across the folded rocks.

5 High tide wave attack undercuts the land at the shoreward end of the platform, causing collapse and creating a sea cliff which continually retreats landwards. Active collapse maintains steep, bare-rocked cliffs.

coastal plateau

former land surface

high tide

low tide

ATLANTIC

Warren Cliff

wave cut platform

9

ⓘ Bear Rock resists the waves

Warren Beach seems to fit the scenario proposed on page 9 very well but looking immediately to the north or south, the rocky shore seems anything but a gently sloping *wave-cut platform*. Why is this? One reason is that the rate at which the waves can carve a *shore platform* depends on the degree of resistance offered by the rocks under attack. In particular the thick sandstone beds seem very resistant to erosion whilst mudstone beds are much more susceptible to wave attack.

Stacks and reefs

The tall isolated stack (left) seen across the bay, Bear Rock, demonstrates this very well. Essentially Bear Rock is composed of several alternating beds of sandstone and mudstone. Like all the sedimentary rocks of the district, these beds were laid down in a near-horizontal position. Here, subsequent folding has tilted these beds through 90°, creating a series of vertical sheets. On the side of the bed facing you are fossil ripple marks flagging this as a former sea-floor surface. At Bear Rock, two resistant beds of sandstone sandwich a softer bed of mudstone which has been eroded away by marine processes, leaving the harder sandstone as dramatic upstanding sheets of rock (see left), a spectacular example of 'differential erosion'. All along this coast the beds *strike* or run out at right angles to the cliffs so that tilted sheets of hard sandstone leap seawards in a series of jagged reefs until finally consumed in surf-smoke.

Bear Rock from cliff-top

10

Looking south from Dyer's Lookout towards Bear Rock and Hartland Quay. Paul Lewin 2005

Caves and tunnels

Caves can be regarded as locations where, for some reason, the cliff has proved less resistant than average and so has eroded away prematurely. Is there a pattern in the distribution of caves at the foot of Warren Cliff?

It is no coincidence that most of the caves are located where, either downfolds or upfolds meet the beach (see page 4). Although the ability of the beds to fold so tightly is remarkable, the axis of the fold often fractures, thus providing a zone of weakness that waves can exploit. Air trapped in cracks as waves break against the cliff at high tide can result in '*explosive decompression*' (page 8) which will blast rock from the cliff face and so facilitate the creation and penetration of a cave. The height of the cave is usually limited by wave height at high tide.

Some caves simply exploit the beds of weaker mudstone. The through-cave of Tunnel Slab on your right is an example of this.

Ribs and runnels

The rocky *shore platform* at Warren Beach is an *erosional surface* but even here, low parallel ribs of resistant sandstone, striking seawards, stand proud of the beach. *Abrasion* rounds and polishes the exposed sandstone ribs (above right), which will eventually break off to form new grey pebbles to be added to the cliff-foot *storm beach*.

Less resistant, sandwiched mudstones are eroded more quickly and, on the beach, are represented by long gutters or runnels, often obscured by an infilling of sand. Ancient fractures created narrow zones of weakened rocks. When exposed these weaknesses can be exploited by waves, eroding straight gullies, which here cross the ribs and runnels at steep angles (see right).

Why this view shouts 'extreme exposure'

This is a view of Warren Beach from the top of Warren Cliff. Along the cliff edge are cushions of thrift (sea pinks) and white-flowered sea campion, both tolerant of the strong salt-laden winds of winter storms which lash this coast. They colonise exposed locations where few other plants survive.

Beneath the precipitous cliffs, themselves evidence of exposure to the active erosion by the sea, waves at high tide continue to attack the foot of the cliff. Blocks of mudstone and sandstone fall to the beach. Waves rapidly reduce the fallen mudstone blocks to a fine-grained mud which, when lifted into suspension, drifts out to sea with the tide. The sandstone blocks, usually failing along iron-stained joints (photo left), crash to the beach as angular orange-brown blocks. Tumbled by the waves, the superficial iron-staining is removed and the blocks are rounded into polished grey pebbles which are pushed against the cliff and banked into a *storm beach*. In time, even these hard grey pebbles will be reduced to sand.

Seawards of the *storm beach*, ribbed beds of raw rock are exposed. Worn by the vigour of storm waves, these rocks have been reduced to a rocky platform covered in places by sand, itself the product of turbulent erosion.

Everything here shouts about this coast being one of extreme exposure and violence. All the more remarkable then, that for centuries this beach was the focus of an intense maritime trade. Why was this?

13

A problem of transport

For many centuries, the poor conditions of local roads meant that moving goods overland was slow, unreliable and expensive, particularly for the haulage of bulky materials.

However, for those settlements with access to the sea, sailing craft offered a faster and cheaper option. This was true, not only for bulky goods such as coal, timber or limestone but also for everyday household manufactured goods delivered from local ports as close as Bideford.

Beach Work

The lack of local havens or harbours west of Bideford, encouraged a tradition of 'beach work'. Essentially, when sea conditions allowed, this involved small sailing vessels being run aground at high tide onto shingle or the pebbles of a *storm beach*, unloading their cargo and then, normally, refloating and departing on the next tide. For example, the North Devon coast has a chain of ruined limekilns, located wherever limestone could be unloaded onto a beach. In fact, you are standing near the foundations of one such kiln, seen in the photo (page 15), taken in 1878.

Building a quay

The tradition of beach work seems to have been well-established by the late sixteenth century. At that time West Country ports were becoming increasingly prosperous, exploiting the growing Atlantic trade to the New World. West Country coastal traffic was also expanding rapidly presenting profitable investment opportunities for local landowners who could offer more reliable landing facilities. Within this period, three quays were constructed locally, at Buck's Mills, at Clovelly (page 43) and here at Hartland Quay.

Why choose this site?

Although very exposed, land access to the shore here was relatively easy and adjacent was a flat meadow where harbour facilities could be built. Between the tides, the rocky *wave-cut platform* was reasonably smooth and the cove was protected at its entrance by a large stack, Life Rock (page 8), linked to the shore by a chain of rocks.

Despite these advantages, building the quay was very expensive. The massive foundation stones, some of which you can still see strewn across the site, would have been floated into the cove before being firmly secured to protect against winter storms. Blocks were keyed in with mortar and probably with metal ties secured with molten lead.

A haven for small craft

The protection offered by the quay to small sailing craft is clear but, as in the 1878 photo, 'beach work' continued to be the norm. In the photo, coal is being unloaded into a cart perhaps for storage at the quay before being sold for local distribution.

> *"There was a deep place of water within the bay. So men have thrown out a pier shaped like a human arm to embrace as it were whatsoever vessel may be there. The land clasps the ship to her breast."*
> Rev Stephen Hawker (1805-1875) Parson-poet of Morwenstow.

Smacks, weathering out a storm at high tide, would normally be secured in mid-harbour by stone-weighted ropes, stretched to anchor points along the quay. The flexing of these ropes would absorb most of the power of a choppy sea within the harbour.

Frequent repairs critical

The 16th century quay, like the surrounding cliffs, was subject to all the power of Atlantic waves. Regular and expensive maintenance was necessary to repair the damage of stones thrown at the outer wall by waves (*attrition*) and to ensure that cracks between the huge blocks were always sealed with mortar so that waves could not trap air in any voids, thus allowing *explosive decompression* to blast whole blocks from the quay walls. It was a constant battle.

The end of an era

The port flourished for well over two centuries. However, with improved road transport, the arrival of the railway at Bideford (1855) and agricultural depressions, the second half of the 19th century, saw a serious decline in coastal trade. Small 'beach work' ports were hard hit.

The end was rapid. The quay was severely damaged by a storm in 1887 and although such damage had been repaired in the past, the quay was already an economic liability and so there was little incentive to undertake expensive repairs. The coup de grâce came in 1896 when storms destroyed the remaining limb of the quay leaving but a short stump. Compare the view of 1878 with that of 2004 (page 1).

To move to the next viewpoint, return up the track and walk back through The Street to the lowest car park.

Across the car park on the southern side is a low wall. Leaning on this wall you have a good view of Well Beach and Screda Point beyond.

When, in 1780, this complex of buildings was prospering as a port there were six cellars (warehouses), a shop, four houses, a malt house and an extensive granary (used to hold corn for export). Most of these buildings, in one form or another, have survived.

Well Beach gets its name from the old well, housed in the small rectangular stone structure with a wooden door, in the corner of the car park at the bottom of the hill.

Well Beach Cliff

The folds so dramatically displayed on the face of Warren Cliff are here partly obscured by a cone of loose rock debris, *scree*. A field sketch of this cliff in October 1987 shows no such debris cone, (see 'Geology at Hartland Quay', page 36).

Unexpectedly, in January 1988, a massive cliff failure caused thousands of tonnes of rock to be detached from the cliff. The rocks cascaded to the cliff foot, spilling out over the *storm beach*. Overnight the cliff top had retreated several metres.

By September 1989, the toe of scree had already been truncated by waves.

A cycle of erosion

This incident set in motion a cycle of events which will, in all probability, return the cliff to a profile which will eventually encourage further failures.

This cliff fall was precipitated, not by waves actually undercutting the cliff (there is no evidence of this on the 1987 field sketch), but by wave action simply removing basal support from the cliff, probably already weakened by weathering processes aided by percolating water. The resulting over-steepening of the cliff profile would be enough to cause slope failure. One consequence of the creation of a cone of debris is that until this apron is removed by waves, the cliff foot will be protected against further wave attack.

At the time of your visit how much of the cliff has been re-exposed? When will the next cliff failure occur? How fast is the cliff eroding? How long is a piece of string?

ⓘ How fast are these cliffs eroding?

Even in this exposed location the erosion of the scree and its reduction to fragments small enough to be removed or redistributed by waves may take some time, not least because, when waves remove the toe of the cone, old scree slopes and former sites of cliff failure may be reactivated.

Another factor controlling how rapidly active solid-rock cliff erosion is resumed, is the height of the cliff. The higher the cliff the bigger the cone of debris produced by a cliff fall and therefore the longer it will take the waves to remove this debris and reach the solid cliff foot again.

On the other hand, the more frequent and stronger the waves, the faster the process of attacking, removing and redistributing the debris will operate. Atlantic-facing cliffs are high wave energy environments and are usually sites being rapidly modified by waves, although coves offer some shelter from the full ferocity of attack.

The 1988 cliff failure at Well Beach was certainly a spectacular episode (a high intensity event) and one where the land loss at the top of the cliff could be measured reasonably accurately. However, in such hard rock areas these incidents do not happen very often (they have low frequency). Moreover they do not occur regularly.

Calculation of the rate at which the cliff is retreating, based upon past events is therefore difficult, particularly when there are so few accurate records. However, measurements in similar hard rock, high wave energy environments suggests that a rough estimate would be just over a metre every 25 years. We can use this figure when we speculate later!

Well Beach is very similar to Warren Beach. If you read the introduction at Warren Beach you may find some pleasure in identifying a similar coastal landscape here. To help, the numbered features are on the photo overleaf!

	A collection of iron-stained rock debris from the cliff, *scree*.
	A cave located on zone of weakness along the axis of a fold.
	A cave resulting from premature erosion of a softer mudstone bed.
1	A *wave-cut platform*, uneven, but nevertheless an *erosion surface*.
2	A *storm beach*; grey pebbles plus some fallen angular brown blocks.
3	Hard sandstone beds exposed as tilted sheets - a *structural surface*.
4	Tilted sandstone beds striking out to sea as jagged reefs.
5	Fresh orange-brown solid rock exposed in cliff after rock-fall.
6	The headland of Screda Point.
7	The conical hill of St Catherine's Tor.
8	A horizontal *erosional surface* forming a lower part of Screda Point.

ⓘ Reading the landscape

There is a fascination in recognising characteristics in a scene which hint at how a landscape might have evolved; a skill which could be called 'reading the landscape'.

In this cove, modern *depositional surfaces* such as a sandy shore, a *storm beach (2)* or a cliff-foot *scree* can all be directly associated with processes happening in the landscape today.

Other landshapes owe their form to the nature or structure of the rocks themselves. For example, the beds of hard sandstone are responsible for the slanting sheets of bare rock which in places form reefs (4) or whole cliff faces (3). These landforms can be called '*structural surfaces*'.

'*Erosional surfaces*', such as a *wave-cut platform* (1) can be linked to a modern *agent of erosion* (wave action). Other erosional surfaces, such as *plateaux*, are relict features, inherited from the past, when environmental conditions were very different. However, both are surfaces which have been planed down to a base level by *agents of erosion* which have cut straight across the folded rock surface beneath.

Recognising 'surfaces' helps to explain landscape history. It can also draw attention to anomalies. For example, (8) has all the characteristics of an *erosional surface* but is it clear what erosional process is or was responsible for its creation?

To walk to the next viewpoint, take the steep path which leaves the road at the foot of the hill or, if you prefer, follow the road up to the grassy field which serves as the middle car park (see rear cover map).

Looking across Well Beach towards Screda Point (page 18), the flat surface (8) defies immediate explanation.

As you walk to viewpoint C you might enjoy turning over in your mind what process, natural or otherwise, could have created the little tableland shown in Paul Lewin's painting?

At the southern end of this field, cliff-top landslips, subsequent to the 1988 cliff failure, have swept away this section of an old track which we will eventually follow south towards Speke's Mouth. Follow the signs for the coastal footpath which direct you away from the dangerous cliff edge and onto the track which contours a small combe. Passing over the stile you enter a coastal nature reserve - keep to the track.

As you walk, enjoy the panoramas of Well Beach and Screda Point. Pause when you have a good view of the horizontal surface across the top of Screda Point. We will call this viewpoint C.

Screda Point Tableland

Just below the surface of this grassy field is a near-horizontal rock surface that cuts straight across the steeply folded beds of rock.

This rock plane is best described as an *erosional surface* but eroded by what? Suggestions are listed below, or you may have a better idea?

What made this headland flat?

FOR	AGAINST

A JCB? - in other words this is an artificial surface

Coastal constructions, including light-houses or military defences were often constructed on sites levelled to ensure suitable foundations.	Hartland Quay car park seems to have a similar 'level' surface. There is also another 'level' surface on the next headland to the south!

WAVES? - cut by waves when sea level was higher

The level of the sea was higher in the past (see page 46) and *wave-cut platforms* were carved at those higher sea levels. Could the top of the headland be a former stack?	Are the other surfaces seen along the coast all at the same level, i.e. linked to one former sea level? Do these former *wave-cut platforms* slope gently towards low tide level?

A LANDSLIP? - land slipping from the coastal *plateau*

Rock failure on steep slopes can result in a coherent mass of solid rock slowly sliding down a slope along a fault or shear surface. The top of the displaced mass can sometimes persist as a grassy surface 'riding' down the slide.	Odd for each headland to have 'failed' in the same way? No sign of shears or faults that might be involved? These failures are often rotational, the shear being curved in profile so the displaced mass, including the grass, is tilted backwards.

A RIVER? - A rock-based floor of a river valley

The rock cross-section (8), as seen from the Quay car park, is typical of an eroding, meandering stream which will cut a near-flat *erosional surface* in the rock as the stream scythes across the valley from side to side. The top metre is a *depositional surface*, perhaps a flood plain?	A river valley? - Where is the river? Which direction was it flowing? Where did it come from? Rivers always flow downhill. How do we get a stream to operate on the top of this headland? Well, If you think this idea is still tenable, you should address these questions!

Try weighing these options up as you walk the next section of the path.

The perils of a lee shore

Looking seawards, it doesn't take much imagination to recognise that this is a treacherous shore for shipping and no more so than for the ketches and schooners which plied this coast in the days of sail. One may romance about wreckers and smugglers but geology and climate conspired to create the real death-trap here for any sailing ship in trouble off these cliffs.

The rocks on this coast *strike* or run out at right angles to the shore, so the hard reefs of sandstone claw out into the sea, claiming any vessel tacking too close to the shore. Except for small vessels, which might make it to Hartland Quay to ride out the storm within the harbour pool, there is no shelter beneath the near continuous Atlantic cliffs on the western side of the Hartland peninsula.

From a Hartland Sketchbook. RJ Lloyd (circa 1967)

Each (cove) has its black field of jagged shark's-tooth rock which paves the cove from side to side, streaked with here and there a pink line of shell-sand, and laced with white foam from the eternal surge, stretching in parallel lines out to the westward, in strata set upright on edge, or tilted towards each other at strange angles by primeval earthquakes - such is the "mouth," as those coves are called; and such the jaw of teeth which they display, one rasp of which would grind abroad the timbers of the stoutest ship. To landward, all richness, softness, and peace; to seaward, a waste and howling wilderness of rock and roller, barren to the fisherman, and hopeless to the shipwrecked mariner.

Description of Hartland coast.   Charles Kingsley's "Westward Ho!" 1855.

As if the geology were not enough to contend with, the climate frustrates the efforts of even the most able of seaman under sail. The prevailing winds are commonly on-shore, driving in from the Atlantic and frequently making this a feared 'lee shore', one where sailing vessels have rocks on their lee side, the side to which they are naturally driven by the wind. As an 11-year old cabin boy on his father's ketch, 'Alpha', William Slade remembers, in 1903, being becalmed about five miles south of here, close to the reefs just off Sharpnose Point (see photograph below).   From "Out of Appledore" by William Slade:

The weather looked black and threatening... Suddenly we were struck by a north-west gale. All hands were standing by and the sails were let down very smartly. It had to be done quickly. The vessel went over on her bulwarks with a lee shore and treacherous rocks close to us.

Father put his arm round me and his words were full of affection and tragedy, "You'll never see mother again." It sounded pretty grim, but I still remembered Father's stories of his experiences, and, strange as it may seem, I was not afraid. I once again trusted him and once again he proved himself a man. The ship seemed to recover somewhat after the first gust had struck her and Father leaped into action like a tiger. The crew responded to his orders in quick time. The first order came, "Set the fore staysail!" This was done and

the mate came back aft evidently badly scared, but he didn't have a chance to think. The next order was, "Shake a reef out of the mainsail," and I can remember everything seemed to be straining to bursting point. The lee mainrail was in the water and Hartland Light close under the lee bow.

"Shake a reef out of the mizzen and jump to it. It's neck or nothing."... Father stood at the wheel his teeth clenched. How she stood that battering I have never understood, but just as they thought it was impossible to weather the Tings (see page 2) she seemed to creep to windward and she did clear, but I afterwards understood it was by an alarmingly small margin, and only the fact that she took the ebb tide under the lee bow in the last moments saved her from smashing to pieces on the rocks which would have been inevitable death to every one of us.

The Atlantic Wall

ADMIRALTY CAUTION FOR SAILING VESSELS   (West Coast of England) 1902

In the approach to the Bristol Channel, there is always a ground swell setting in from about W.N.W., unless easterly winds have long prevailed... Its effect is to impel a vessel towards the Cornish ... or Devonshire coast. It is worthy of remark that with the wind westward of South there is scarcely a safe roadstead for a sailing vessel between Land's End and Flatholm island in the Bristol Channel, with the exception of Lundy and Clovelly roads...

Should a sailing vessel (become embayed), the crew should stick to their ship, as, with the many life-saving appliances established along the coast, there is every chance of being saved. There is little or no chance of saving life by taking to the ship's boats, owing to the heavy and confused sea, which at times renders even life-boats unmanageable.

The walls of the Wreckers Bar and relics in the Shipwreck Museum at Hartland Quay graphically testify to the perils for sailing ships on a lee shore armed with row upon row of sharp sandstone reefs set at right angles to the shore each probing out to sea before disappearing into the surf. These reefs continue to claim ships long after the days of sail. In November 1962, the Green Ranger, a 3000-ton Fleet Auxiliary Tanker was under tow when, in heavy seas, the cable parted and she struck Gunpath Reef (see left) beneath the 110m cliffs of Milford Common (see page 41). The skeleton crew of seven 'stuck to their ship' and were rescued from the cliff-foot by breeches-buoy. Some of the more valuable metal parts of the ship were eventually winched to the cliff top. The port-holes now decorate the Wreckers Bar at Hartland Quay, which for many years after 1962 was called the 'Green Ranger' Bar.

D   Wargery Water Cascade

When you are ready to continue walk along the coast path which gently descends southwards.

After about 100 metres the path reaches the mouth of the small stream known as Wargery Water.

Pause by the termination of the stream. Be aware of the proximity of the dangerous cliff edge.
This is viewpoint D.

As you walk, notice to your right, is another small headland, very similar to Screda Point, again with a flat middle section. The rocks exposed on the side of the headland suggests that this is another *erosion surface*.

Also notice the small spring on the left which oozes water onto the path. This is the site of Bradstone's Well, said to cure scurvy and sore eyes, even so, don't risk a drink.

A coastal hanging valley

Wargery Water is unusual in that the mouth of the valley is perched above the beach - a coastal hanging valley. The stream ends abruptly as a waterfall which cascades over the edge of the cliff (D) and onto the pebbles below.

Over a long period, by erosion or deposition, rivers and streams have a tendency to

Looking north from St Catherine's Tor towards Screda Point and Hartland Quay

adjust the gradient of the valley floor over which they flow, eventually creating a smooth energy-efficient slope which grades gently towards the sea - a graded profile. A well-graded river or stream, by the time it reaches its mouth, is at sea level and will gently flow into the sea.

A stream which deviates from this gentle 'graded' long profile suggests there is something unusual about the history of the valley.

So, why does the gentle gradient of Wargery Water end so abruptly?

The Hartland Peninsula. *It contains the most impressive cliff scenery in England and Wales, above all the iron coast from Hartland Point southwards, with its coastal waterfalls. The seascapes are superb, for there is no land between this coast and America.* WG Hoskins 1954.

Although the remarkable scenery of this coast has been the cause of wonder and speculation for many generations, the first modern authoritative examination of the coastal landscape to be published was by the geologist Newell Arber in 1911.

He came to this coast in the early years of the 20th century, determined to write a book dealing solely with the nature and origin of this coast-line,

"expressed in as simple a language as possible which might interest those who visit North Devon and North Cornwall."

The Coast Scenery of North Devon by EA Newell Arber (1911) remains a classic to this day.

Below is Newell Arber's explanatory commentary on the section of coast which we have just walked.

If we examine the present mouth of this stream [D] we shall find that while the stream itself goes over the cliff, the nearly level bottom of the valley, and also one of its walls continues along the cliff to Hartland Quay. The (100 foot) contour of this landward wall is shown on the map [right]. We shall also find that it is possible to trace portions of the wall on the seaward side, in the shape of low mounds at the extremities of some of the small promontories.

At the point where the present waterfall is found [D], this valley formerly bent a little more to the North, and ran parallel to the coast. While the landward wall has remained intact, the sea has captured nearly the whole of the opposite wall, with the exceptions of the low mounds of Screda Point and Hartland Quay. At one time, no doubt, this stream flowed out on to Warren Beach.

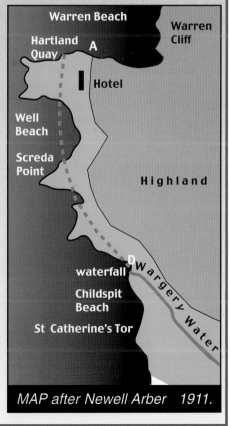

MAP after Newell Arber 1911.

25

To reach viewpoint E, follow the footpath beside the stream. On your right rises the conical hill of St Catherine's Tor. Shortly after leaving Wargery Waterfall there is a large earth bank which stretches across the valley floor.

Today this earthen bank, wide enough to have a byre cut into it, is simply a field boundary. However, although modified, it is thought originally to be a medieval dam constructed by the monks of Hartland Abbey, near Stoke. The shallow lake thus created was used principally as a swannery. The Abbey was dissolved by Henry VIII in 1539 but its was reportedly still in use as a fishery if not a swannery in 1760. A strandline track on the western side, beneath St Catherine's Tor, suggests that, at the time the lake was in use, the water was not deep.

Passing through the gate / stile, continue to follow Wargery Water upstream until, after about 120 metres, the path crosses the stream by concrete stepping stones. Pause on the far side. This is viewpoint E.

The stream wanders across the exceptionally flat, wide valley floor, but upstream Wargery Water becomes much more confined within a narrow, steep-sided valley with little flood plain.

St Catherine's Tor

To the seaward side of the stepping stones is St Catherine's Tor, named after a mariners' chapel that reputedly once crowned its summit but which has long ago been lost to the sea. The top of St Catherine's Tor is 84 metres above sea level. Its flanks are impressively steep with a long regular slope standing at an angle of about 32 degrees.

The shape of the tor is remarkable because of its isolation, separated from the rest of the coast by the flat plain upon which you are standing.

The dry flat plain on the southern side of the Tor ends abruptly, overlooking Speke's Mill Mouth Beach. The scene is captured in Paul Lewin's painting (right) with St Catherine's Tor rising to the right and Wargery Water in the immediate foreground. To the south the coast marches away towards the Cornish border.

You may feel that this dry flat field adds an additional complication to the story of Wargery Water and the sea. If you still find the role of landscape interpreter exhilarating, then you might like, before reading on, to consider the origins of this dry 'valley'.

The curious flat plain naturally attracted the attention of Newell Arber as he walked along this coast.

Looking south across Speke's Mill Mouth. Paul Lewin

"Southward beyond Wargery Water, we see St Catherine's Tor, a bold cliff which is really a seaward wall of a tributary valley of Wargery Water, now beheaded by the sea and quite dry... This is another instance of a sea-dissected valley, but in this case the head, and not the foot, has disappeared beneath the Atlantic"

Newell Arber, 1911.

Because of the size of the 'valley' to the south of St Catherine's Tor, we might speculate that it was the smaller Wargery Water that was a tributary to this larger, now dry valley, rather than the other way round.

F   Arthur's Path

To reach viewpoint F, Arthur's Path, cross the flat field ahead of you, with Wargery Water on your left and ahead, an earth-baked stone wall through which a stile gives access to the next field. Beyond the stile, the path swings right and begins to climb diagonally southwards across the hillside.

When you have nearly achieved the top of the hill, but still have a good view back northwards towards St Catherine's Tor and beyond, pause. This we will call viewpoint F, Arthur's Path.

Here is a reconstruction of how St Catherine's Tor just might have looked, viewed from Arthur's Path during an episode of the Ice Age.

Did glaciers reach Devon?

There is little to indicate that any ice sheet came far enough south in the Quaternary Ice Age to cover Devon and Cornwall. However, rock debris from the margins of one or more former ice sheets have been identified at Fremington, near Barnstaple and on the Scilly Isles off the coast of Cornwall. This has led to the suggestion that during at least one stage during the Quaternary, an ice sheet may have spread far enough south to abut against what is today the north coast of Devon and Cornwall.

In such a situation one can imagine (above) water melting from the ice cap being trapped between the land rising to the south and the thick ice-sheet rising away to the north-west over what is today the Bristol Channel. Meltwater, trapped between headlands, might escape by pouring along the coast, carving a channel along any convenient route available.

Meltwater channels

What do modern meltwater channels look like? By virtue of the great volume of water they carry at certain times of the year, when a lot of ice and snow are melting, meltwater channels on the margins of modern ice sheets are characterised by having wide 'flat' floors maintaining a fairly constant width and having very steep sides.

When eventually abandoned by meltwater, such channels are frequently left 'dry' and cut across present-day drainage patterns.

Attention has been drawn to the similarity of the shape between the 'valley' behind St Catherine's Tor and known meltwater channels in Wales and elsewhere.

This similarity was sufficiently intriguing for the Quaternary Research Association to include the 'valley' in a field excursion which visited Hartland Quay in 1974. A guide book was prepared for participants. The section relevant to this coast read as follows:

"Of all the possible ice-marginal or subglacial channels which have been described briefly (Stephens,1966), those near Hartland Quay (GR: SX 225243) and Damehole Point (GR: SX 226263) are perhaps the most convincing examples. At both sites channels have been incised in such a way as to isolate a small hill on the seaward side of the channel, and throughout their length the channels 'hang' above the sea. The channels are characterised by flat floors, frequently overlain by 1.8 to 2.4 metres (6-8 feet) of coarse, blocky head."

"The 'in and out' channels at Hartland Quay and Damehole Point are not marine-cut features, but probably form part of the seaward ends of a system of coastal valleys, which have been linked together and widened appreciably by water flowing along the edge, or below the margin, of an ice mass impinging against the coast. It is conceivable therefore that the channels were formed when ice was depositing till at Fremington, Trebetherick Point and on the Scilly Isles; subsequently they received a thin layer of head during the last glacial period."

N Stephens,
Quaternary Research Association, Easter 1974

Evidence, in the form of glacial debris, has never been found here and the theory that this valley has been modified by glacial meltwater remains highly speculative. However, the origin of this enigmatic, steep-sided, misfit 'valley' remains to be fully resolved, perhaps to be revealed at our next stop?

St Catherine's Tor

The photograph above, taken from the *plateau* edge to the north of St Catherine's Tor looking south, covers the last three viewpoints visited, including where you now stand. It gives another perspective to the flat green fields surrounding St Catherine's Tor.

In the foreground is the earth bank which probably once dammed Wargery Water to form a shallow lake.

Coastal erosion on the seaward side of St Catherine's Tor has carved a precipitous arête above Childspit Beach. Dark shadows on the landward side of the tor help to emphasise just how steep and regular is this hillside slope.

Wave-cut platform

The photo (right) looks seawards from the summit of St Catherine's Tor. It reminds us just how wide the *wave-cut platform* is along this coast, 250 metres at this point, a reflection of the amount of coastal erosion that must have taken place.

Shore Platform

Breaking waves are not the only process that erode *wave-cut platforms*. Other shore processes include the constant wetting and drying of the rocks, the effect of boring animals, solution and the growth of salt crystals in rock cracks as they dry out. All help to break up the rock surface on the shore. For this reason, these rocky platforms may more accurately be described simply as *shore platforms*.

Continue to follow the coastal path south over the brow of the hill, perhaps pausing for the fine view over the valley of the Milford Water. When you are ready, descend the steep coastal path into the valley which ends abruptly at Speke's Mill Mouth.

The first attraction is perhaps to walk, slightly inland, over to the fence, where you may stand to look down on the Milford Water as it descends some 48 metres to the beach. Care is needed for, when wet, the rock is slippery, as is the polished, tufty grass.

"Undoubtedly, when the existence of this fall becomes better known, it will be the object of pilgrimage."

EA Newell Arber, 1911

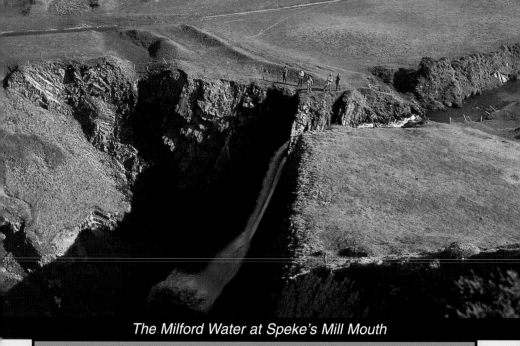

The Milford Water at Speke's Mill Mouth

ⓘ A geological description of the falls

The Milford Water descends to the beach in a series of falls and cascades. The lip of the first fall is a near-vertical bed of hard sandstone which has offered considerable resistance to any down-cutting by the stream.

The first fall plunges 16 metres down this bed of sandstone, which is the eastern limb of a tight downfold (syncline). At the foot of the first fall the stream then turns at right angles, guided south along the axis of the downfold before breaking through the western limb of the fold and tumbling in several small cascades across an upfold (anticline) towards the beach and the sea.

This is a very good example of a structurally-controlled waterfall, one where the route the water takes is clearly linked to the structure of the rocks. However, it is worth considering why this waterfall is located here in the first place?

The vertical bed of hard sandstone has resisted the down-cutting stream, but is this really responsible for the way the stream is perched above the beach?

Given the otherwise smooth long profile of the stream upstream from the waterfall, this abrupt truncation of the smooth long profile looks like another example of a coastal hanging valley, the result of the valley being captured by the sea advancing on the land.

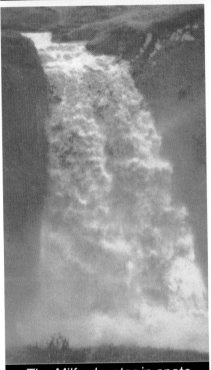

The Milford water in spate after a winter storm.

The valley ends abruptly at the waterfall and this provides a clear cross-section of the valley floor and sides. As at Screda Point, the floor of the valley is a solid rock horizontal *erosion surface,* masked by a thin veneer of *head.* Again, this surface was cut straight across the folded rocks as the stream meandered from side to side. Whenever a meander impinged on the valley sides, the erosional plane was extended a little more. On the valley sides (see page 32), the solid rock slopes are both steep and regular, just like St Catherine's Tor and Screda Point. They all stand at an angle of about 32°.

This waterfall looks more and more like another case of a valley captured by the sea. If this is the case the height of this coastal 'hanging valley' (48 metres above the beach) suggests that the valley must have originally extended a considerable distance, if originally, it flowed gently down into the sea.

Now leave the fence and move carefully towards the cliff overlooking Speke's Mill Beach. Stop at the top of a steep cliff-cut path which leads down to the beach.

A donkey track

The zig-zag path to the shore below was once used by donkeys to collect sand from the beach. The sand was held in sand lews (open storage pens), still seen on the northern side of the valley floor. From here, before the days of artificial fertilisers, the sand was distributed to local farmers and applied to their heavy acid soils. Now turn to look out to sea.

Missing head & foot?

It is astonishing to consider the amount of land that must have disappeared beneath the Atlantic. In the case of the Milford Water the whole of the lower course of the stream (the foot of the system) is missing. In the case of Newell Arber's mysterious tributary on the south side of St Catherine's Tor it was the upper course (the head of the system) that is missing.

Making connections

Looking north, it might have already occurred to you that, with one mighty meander sweep, a former connection across the bay from the lip of Speke's Mill Mouth to the dry flat area behind St Catherine's Tor looks a distinct possibility. This would connect the the truncated Milford Water with the beheaded Newell Arber 'tributary'. You may have recognised this possible connection already but if not, rest assured, you are in good company, for Newell Arber, despite having examined the coast in some detail, did not recognise the possibility of this final spectacular link.

The visual landscape evidence may seem quite convincing, even more so perhaps if you refer back to the photograph on page 30.

So the green field surrounding the landward side of St Catherine's Tor can be interpreted as the broad sweep of a former meander. Next, beyond St Catherine's Tor in the photo on page 30, imagine a similar mirror-image meander curving out across Speke's Mill Mouth Bay before swinging back to meet the valley of the Milford Water, just where you are now standing.

Testing out the idea

Recognising the probable sequence of events which led to some of the most spectacular landscape features along this coast might be regarded as a good example of how you can 'read a landscape'. However, such an idea should be supported by scientific evidence. How could this hypothesis be tested?

One suggestion might be to look for river sediments along the supposed former course of the stream. Similarities in the composition of these sediments might link the isolated remnants of the proposed former river system. Unfortunately such sedimentalogical connections have not yet been identified.

Another suggestion might be to project the smooth long profile of the valley of the Milford Water and see if the curve of this graded profile matches the traces of surviving valley floor, behind St Catherine's Tor and beyond.

Some years ago Oxford Polytechnic students, using accurate levelling devices, constructed the section shown on the next page. The resulting smooth long profile from this survey does seem to confirm that such a connection existed.

The graded long profile (P-Q-R-S-T-U) also confirms that we are not looking at a series of raised beaches or former wave-cut platforms.

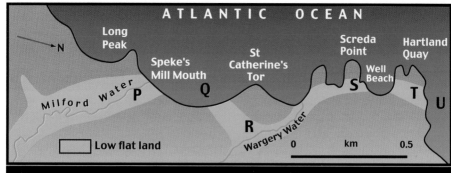

Above: The probable course of the Milford Water from Speke's Mill Mouth to Hartland Quay and Warren Beach

Below: A long profile of the floor of the Milford Water and its probable extension

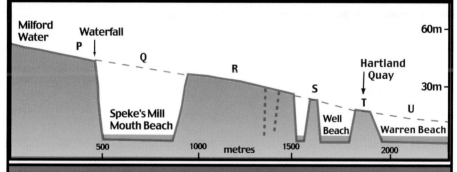

When did all this happen?

When did this 'river capture' happen? Well, that would be pure speculation but anyway, it would be fun to try and estimate when capture occurred!

Using the rate of cliff retreat suggested on page 17 (let's call it five metres every 100 years) and taking the proposed meander across Speke's Mill Mouth Bay as being the mirror image with the same dimensions as the one which curves behind St Catherine's Tor, it is possible to estimate the date when

the sea breached the course of the Milford Water. This puts the time, give or take a few hundred years, as nightfall preceding 23 October 6 BC.

So, it is possible that, from a passing galley sailing around the 'Promontory of Hercules' (Hartland Point), Roman sailors saw the Milford Water in spate just at the time it was diverted by the encroaching sea. The event is not recorded!

Ice Age inheritance

In describing the evolution of this coast, the emphasis has been on the interaction between modern marine processes and the local rocks. However it would be difficult to 'read' this landscape with any hope of a satisfactory outcome without considering what this scenery has inherited from a period when cold climate processes severely modified the local topography leaving relics which have survived into today's landscape.

In particular we might consider the role of the last cold stage of the Ice Age, the Devensian (see page 46), which was at its coldest only some 18,000 years ago.

Arctic tundra

As we have previously suggested, there is little evidence for an ice sheet ever covering mainland Devon and Cornwall but nevertheless, during the coldest stages of the last Ice Age this area was only some 70km from the edge of the vast Welsh ice-sheet and experienced *periglacial* (peripheral to the ice) conditions of arctic-like tundra where the ground was deep frozen with only short summer superficial thaws. Under such conditions, vegetation was reduced to mosses, lichens and perhaps creeping willows which could survive the cold winters.

Frost action

When not frozen solid, water in the soil penetrated any available rock joints, and there, by repeatedly freezing and thawing could fragment the rocks. This, together with frost heave, created a surface layer of angular broken stones embedded within a background of finer material (*head*).

Sliding summer slopes

During the coldest stages of the last ice age, the ground was permanently deep-frozen (permafrost), although the top metre or so of the surface experienced a short-lived thaw each brief summer. Water, melting from the winter's snowfall, together with melting ground-ice, being unable to percolate down into the still-frozen deeper ground was confined to the uppermost layer of *head* which it rapidly saturated.

Lubricated with water and driven by gravity, this pasty mess oozed downslope, a process known as *solifluction*, at a rate of between 10-100cm each summer season. On the gentler valley floors the slope debris began to collect, overwhelming the capacity of local streams to wash it away and so it gradually infilled the local valleys with an unconsolidated mass of *head*, over 20 metres thick in places.

Streams fight back

By the time the last cold stage ended, about 10,000 years ago (see page 46), many local valleys had accumulated a thick infilling of *head* which overlaid the horizontal rock of the valley floor. In the post ice-age climatic amelioration, frost action and *solifluction* decreased to the point where local streams, no longer choked with more debris than they could handle, were able to carve down into the *head*, often leaving terraces on either side of their valleys.

Further walks

There are no clear examples of such terraces on this walk but one, Blackpool Mill on the Abbey River, can be visited from Hartland Quay being only a kilometre northwards on the coastal path (see page 39).

The reason why there are no good examples on this walk is itself of interest. The depth of *head* infilling the valley at Marsland Mouth is over 20 metres (see references, page 48), yet the depth of valley floor *head* at Speke's Mill Mouth and Screda Point is barely one metre. Why is this? Well, perhaps, with a larger catchment than the smaller combes, the Milford Water may have been powerful enough to flush away the unconsolidated *head* debris which had accumulated in its valley. If you catch the Milford Water after a winter storm (photo, page 33), you will be impressed enough to believe this!

Inherited slopes

As noted, many local hill slopes have long steep rectilinear mid-sections standing at angles between 29° and 32°. The angle at which these slopes stand is a reflection of the limiting angle of stability of the debris, which in turn is related to the size and angularity of the debris and the amount of water it contains. In this district this 'stable' angle is about 31°.

Straight slopes are to be expected where rapid downslope movement of debris is faster than the creation of new debris. Frost-liberated *head*, *soliflucted* downslope in a *periglacial* climate, produces just such conditions. Any rock exposed through the thin layer of *head* would be more susceptible to frost attack than that buried beneath the thin layer of *head*. In this way, solid irregularities would be removed progressively and a regular (straight) rock slope would develop, buried beneath a superficial protecting layer of broken rubble (*head*).

Straight slopes can be formed wherever the base of a slope is being undercut, perhaps by the sea or by a river. However, the frequency of straight slopes locally suggests many were created under cold conditions and have survived because, when the climate eventually got warmer, chemical weathering, that replaced the mechanical frost activity, had little effect on landforms, so old forms survived, inherited from the colder past.

Looking up the valley

The steep-sided combe of the Milford Water is notched into the edge of the high but gently sloping coastal *plateau*. The stream meanders towards you across its rock-floored flood plain. Woodlands shrink back from the approaching salt-laden winds of the exposed Atlantic coast.

... " *those delightful glens, which cut the high tableland of the confines of Devon and Cornwall, and opening each through its gorge of down and rock, towards the boundless western ocean. Each is like the other, and each is like no other English scenery. Each has its upright walls, inland of rich oak-wood, nearer the sea of dark green furze, then of smooth turf, then of weird, black cliffs which range out right and left far into the deep sea, in castles, spires, and wings of jagged iron-stone.* "

From 'The Coombes of the Far West' in Charles Kingsley's,
Westward Ho! 1855

That ends the more formal part of this 'landscape companion'. If you are returning directly to Hartland Quay, the most direct route is to retrace the path of your outward journey. If you were unaware of it before you started out, as you reach the hotel at Hartland Quay, you may pause to wonder at its river-bed location. Some other options of extending your exploration of the district are outlined on the next few pages.

Where will you walk now?

❑ **The beach at Speke's Mill Mouth.**

If you venture down the zig-zag path to the beach at Speke's Mill Mouth extra care is needed. This is not part of the coastal footpath. Do not attempt to return to Hartland Quay along the cliff foot as, even at low tide, high seaward-running reefs make this a hazardous venture.

❑ **Walking south from Speke's Mill Mouth**

If you decide to continue your walk further south, walk upstream for about 200 metres where a footbridge spans the Milford Water. The signposted coastal path climbs south to the cliff-top where the coastal *plateau* provides easy walking for several kilometres. However, unless you have made provision to be picked up at a convenient point (see page 2), you will need to return by the same route. The following two pages review some of the scenery to be seen to the south of here.

❑ **Blackpool Mill**

To visit the mouth of the Abbey River at Blackpool Mill (see below), return to Hartland Quay and then take the coastal footpath northwards. After about a kilometre, the coastal path drops to a footbridge over the Abbey River, the mouth of which is overlooked by river terraces. A path leads to a pleasant cove and beach.

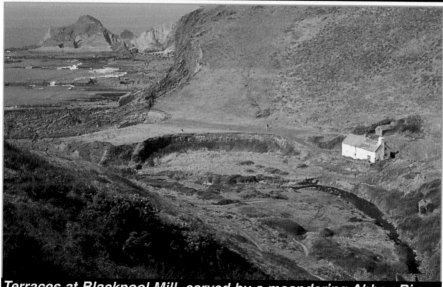

Terraces at Blackpool Mill, carved by a meandering Abbey River.
Location: One km north of Hartland Quay on the coastal path.

Crossing the Milford Water by footbridge, the path climbs the flank of a small tributary valley southwards. Before long, a sweeping panorama back along the coast (above) includes the whole of your walk so far.

A little further south, beyond Longpeak (see page 2), you reach the coastal *plateau* at Milford Common and walking is easy for a while. The gentle surface hides the zig-zag folds in the rocks beneath your feet (see below).

From the 110m cliffs you can look down upon Gunpath Reef which caught the Green Ranger in 1952 (see page 23). Driven shorewards, the ship gradually broke apart but for many years the boiler and pistons could be visited at low tide.

Beyond Milford Common, the cliff-top path overlooks Elmscott Cliffs and the rocky shore below. Paul Lewin's painting (left) shows this shore at half-tide.

Finally, before the coastal path drops to Welcombe Mouth and Strawberry Water, pause at Embury Beacon, some 700 metres south of Nabor Point.

Below, from Embury Beach (see page 6) the cliff face folds are again in sharp contrast to the gentle *plateau* surface over which you have been walking.

Although easy to miss at ground level, Embury Beacon has a cliff-top ramparted iron-age earthworks, dated to about 100 BC. Seen from a helicopter, the complex is clear! Although described as a 'promontory fort', the precarious cliff-hanging position of the inner ramparts, again serves to demonstrate the active nature of coastal erosion along side, the Atlantic side, of the Hartland Peninsula.

Coastlines of contrast

Even on this short walk, the characteristics of the Hartland Heritage coast grow familiar and it becomes almost second nature to 'read the landscape' for signs which explain the land-shapes and the way the coastline has dramatically eroded.

Yet, only a few miles away on the other side of the 'peninsula', the coastal landscape presents an entirely different picture. To experience this contrast, try walking down the cobbled street to the shore at Clovelly (see map, page 2).

Clovelly, like Hartland, once boasted active limekilns and an old quay which still survives, although the days of tidal 'beach work' have gone.

If you walk along the pebble *storm beach* to the west of the quay you will soon be standing in the position from which the 2004 photo (below) was shot. The composition of the rocks at this spot is very similar to that at Hartland Quay, yet the coastal scenery and the vegetation look very different. Why is this?

The Hartland Coast

The Hartland coast faces west and takes the full force of Atlantic storms. What is more, winds are most commonly onshore, forcing storm waves against the cliffs. In this 'high-energy wave environment', cliffs are undercut and collapse comparatively rapidly creating fresh-faced steep cliffs.

The Clovelly Coast

The Clovelly coast faces north-east, sheltered from Atlantic winds and although waves are refracted (bent) around Hartland Point they are much weakened by the time they reach this shore. Winds most often blow from the Atlantic so here they are off-shore. On these cliffs, trees can grow right down to the beach. One might ask how active coastal erosion can be on such a sheltered shore? There are always problems when long timescales are involved but here we have some unexpected help from Charles Napier Hemy (1841-1917).

Among the Shingle at Clovelly

A Pre-Raphaelite vision

The artist, Charles Napier Hemy visited Clovelly in 1864. At that time he was attracted to the Pre-Raphaelite school and its preoccupation with the romantic vision of nature, demanding an intimate experience of the natural world and all its intricate visual detail. Pre-Raphaelite landscapes reflected this philosophy by reproducing, in minute detail, the visual complexity of even the humblest of natural objects. We can therefore be confident that Hemy's picture, down to the individual pebbles in the foreground, is as accurate a representation of nature as it is possible to paint.

Then as now

Looking at the crag on the foreshore to the right, the 2004 view looks pretty much the same as that portrayed in the 1864 painting, even though they are separated by 140 years.

It is difficult to distinguish any natural change. We can conclude therefore that, here at least, the sea is relatively ineffective at eroding the cliff, protected though it is by a wide bank of wave-washed pebbles. This seems to confirm that, relative to Hartland, this is a sheltered shore.

However, there is another factor which shapes this coast. The folded rocks at Hartland run or *strike* east-west, at right angles to the shore. This results in caves and steep cliffs and is also responsible for the reefs probing directly into the surf. On the Clovelly coast, rocks still *strike* east-west but on this coast this is parallel to the shore, encouraging sheets of rock to slip or topple towards the shore. These landslips are a characteristic of the coast between Clovelly and Buck's Mills and are meticulously documented in Hemy's painting.

ABRASION The wearing away of rock by the movement of water, wind or ice, armed with debris such as sand, stones or boulders. An example would be waves, armed with stones, attacking the cliff-foot at high tide.

AGENT OF EROSION A useful term which groups the various processes which, when transporting debris, can initiate erosion of the land surface. These 'agents' include rivers, glaciers, wind, waves and currents.

ATTRITION The mutual wear suffered by debris in transport, e.g. stones rubbing against one another on a beach.

DEPOSITIONAL SURFACE Unconsolidated debris, that has been eroded and transported, may be deposited to form a recognisable surface. A good example is a sandy beach. River deposits can create a near-level flood plain. *Head* can create its own sloping depositional landform. Hillside *scree* is often a depositional surface, albeit an unusually steep one.

DIFFERENTIAL EROSION The erosion of rock where the resistance offered is uneven, perhaps because of the composition of the rock; for example local sandstones are more resistant than mudstones. If the rock has previously been weakened by weathering, fracturing, or faulting, then this will create variable susceptibility. The resulting uneven erosion may well be reflected in a whole series of small *structural surfaces*.

EROSION SURFACE A near-level landform or landscape surface created by *agents of erosion,* which planed the land down to a level below which, at the time of formation, they had insufficient energy to downcut further. Local examples include the coastal *plateaux*, wave-cut platforms and the graded solid rock beds of rivers. In contrast, other landforms can be described as *depositional surfaces* or *structural surfaces*. Most of the 'surfaces' that you will see on this walk, big and small, can be fitted into one of these three types.

EXPLOSIVE DECOMPRESSION Waves breaking against a rock may trap air in surface cracks, putting this air under enormous pressure. As the wave recedes, the resulting instantaneous decompression can blast fragments from the rock face.

FREEZE-THAW Water freezing in confined crevices may force a crack to open by up to 9%. Subsequent thawing allows water to penetrate further into the rock. Repeated freeze-thaw action fragments the rock.

HEAD Originally a west country farming term for deep, rubbly subsoil. Here used to describe the mantle of unconsolidated material often derived from frost shattering and transported by *solifluction*.

PERIGLACIAL Literally peripheral to ice masses. Used to describe the very cold arctic-like tundra environments experienced by North Devon during the cold stages of the last ice age when *freeze-thaw*, rock shattering and *solifluction* were major landscape processes.

PLATEAU An upland surface of relatively flat land. In North Devon these plateaux are *erosional surfaces* at about 200-210m, 139-155m and 75-90m.

SCREE An accumulation of fragmented rock waste below a cliff or rock face.

SHORE PLATFORM See *wave-cut platform*.

SOLIFLUCTION The slow downslope flow of surface material and sub-soil when saturated by water. It is most effective in very cold conditions where a permanently frozen sub-soil (permafrost) prevents summer thaw water from percolating down from the surface. Under those circumstances it is often termed 'gelifluction'. The process is effective in transporting downslope huge quantities of *head*.

STORM BEACH The mass of coarse sediment, such as pebbles, that collect at the top of a beach marking the maximum extent of deposition by storm waves. Its coarseness makes it permeable and therefore less likely to be dragged seawards by the backwash of waves.

STRIKE In this book strike it is used rather loosely to indicate the general direction of the folded rock structure but more accurately the direction of strike of an inclined surface of rock is a compass bearing of a horizontal line on that surface. It will be at right angles to the true dip of that surface.

STRUCTURAL SURFACES Landform or landscape surfaces whose shape is largely determined by the structure of the rocks themselves. For example due to *differential erosion* or weathering, resistant beds of sandstone stand out as sheets of rock which significantly contribute to the appearance of reefs, caves and cliff faces.

WAVE-CUT PLATFORM An *erosion surface* gently sloping between high and low water. The term implies a platform cut by waves using available sand or stones, *abrasion*. However, other shore processes including the constant wetting and drying of the rocks, the effect of boring animals, solution and the growth of salt crystals in rock cracks as they dry out. All these help to break up the rock so the term '*shore platform*' is sometimes preferred as it is purely descriptive and does not imply that it was formed by one particular process.

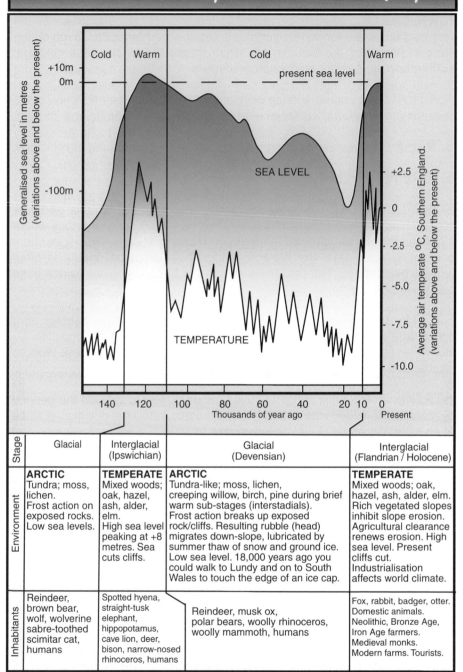

Stage	Glacial	Interglacial (Ipswichian)	Glacial (Devensian)	Interglacial (Flandrian / Holocene)
Environment	**ARCTIC** Tundra; moss, lichen. Frost action on exposed rocks. Low sea levels.	**TEMPERATE** Mixed woods; oak, hazel, ash, alder, elm. High sea level peaking at +8 metres. Sea cuts cliffs.	**ARCTIC** Tundra-like; moss, lichen, creeping willow, birch, pine during brief warm sub-stages (interstadials). Frost action breaks up exposed rock/cliffs. Resulting rubble (head) migrates down-slope, lubricated by summer thaw of snow and ground ice. Low sea level. 18,000 years ago you could walk to Lundy and on to South Wales to touch the edge of an ice cap.	**TEMPERATE** Mixed woods; oak, hazel, ash, alder, elm. Rich vegetated slopes inhibit slope erosion. Agricultural clearance renews erosion. High sea level. Present cliffs cut. Industrialisation affects world climate.
Inhabitants	Reindeer, brown bear, wolf, wolverine sabre-toothed scimitar cat, humans	Spotted hyena, straight-tusk elephant, hippopotamus, cave lion, deer, bison, narrow-nosed rhinoceros, humans	Reindeer, musk ox, polar bears, woolly rhinoceros, woolly mammoth, humans	Fox, rabbit, badger, otter. Domestic animals. Neolithic, Bronze Age, Iron Age farmers. Medieval monks. Modern farms. Tourists.

Acknowledgments

The drawings, 'Atlantic Cliffs' on page 2 and 'Hartland Coast' (inside rear cover) were by the late Jo Keene, artist of Westward Ho! For permission to reproduce illustrative material I thank the following: Paul Lewin of Rose Cottage, Abbotsham for; 'South from St Catherine's Tor across Speke's Mill Mouth' (front cover), 'Bear Rock, Hartland' (page 11), 'Screda Point, low tide, Devon' (page 19), 'South across Speke's Mill Mouth, Devon (page 27) and 'Elmscott Cliffs' (page 41): Reginald Lloyd of Bideford for permission to reproduce a pen and ink drawing from his Hartland Sketchbook (page 21): The Laing Art Gallery (Tyne and Wear Museums) for permission to reproduce 'Among the Shingles at Clovelly' by Charles Napier Hemy (page 43): The U.K. Hydrographic Office, Admiralty Way, Taunton, for undertaking a search identifying the source and providing an accurate copy of the quote which appears on page 23: Alan Lewis of the Hallsannery Centre, Bideford, for the ice age sketch on page 28: Chris Cornford for some geological reassurance: Janet Keene for long-suffering proof reading and so much more. **PHOTOGRAPHY:** 'Climbing the bear' (page 10) is by Janet Keene. 'Revisiting the Green Ranger' (page 40) is by Chris Howes, who, against his better judgement, kayaked this coast with me. All colour photography is by the author. "The Cliffs of Hartland Quay" is a fully revised and extended edition of a booklet of the same name first published by Thematic Trails in 1990. I finish, below, with this small nugget of rock-art to be found on the flanks of Life Rock, Hartland Quay.

Peter Keene (1st February 2006).

47

References and Sources

ARBER, E.A.N. 1911. The Coast Scenery of North Devon. Dent, London.
BURTON, S.H. 1953. The North Devon Coast. Werner Laurie, London.
CHILDS, A. and CORNFORD, C. 1989. Geology at Hartland Quay. Thematic Trails, Oxford.
HOSKINS, W.G. 1954. Devon. Collins, London.
KEENE, P. 1990. Strawberry Water to Marsland Mouth. Thematic Trails, Oxford.
KEENE, P. 1996. Classic Landforms of the North Devon Coast. Geographical Association, Sheffield.
KINGSLEY, C. 1855. Westward Ho! Macmillan, London.
NIX, M. and MYERS, M.R. 1982. Hartland Quay, the story of a vanished port. Hartland Quay Museum, Hartland Quay.
SLADE, W.J. 1959. Out of Appledore. Conway Maritime Press, London.
STEPHENS, N. 1974. Hartland Quay and Damehole Point, in: Quaternary Research Association, Field Handbook, Easter Meeting 1974, Exeter.

Other theme walks on the coast of North Devon

Geology at Hartland Quay
Strawberry Water to Marsland Mouth
The Cliffs of Westward Ho! a sense of time
Westward Ho! Against the Sea
Across the Rocky Shore at Westward Ho!
Northam Burrows estuary environments
Braunton Burrows Ecology Trail
The Cliffs of Saunton
Valley of Rocks, Lynton
Lyn in Flood, Watersmeet to Lynmouth

This selection of walks on the North Devon coast, published by Thematic Trails, may be obtained at information centres, museums and shops local to sites or direct from the publisher.

Thematic Trails
7 Norwood Avenue, Kingston Bagpuize, Oxfordshire OX13 5AD
Tel and Fax: 01865-820522.   e-mail: keene@thematic-trails.org

Ask for free catalogue of 100+ publications or view same on our website:
www.thematic-trails.org
Thematic Trails is a registered educational charity no 801188

The Cliffs of Hartland Quay
Published by Thematic Trails   Printed by Witney Press
Copyright Peter Keene 2006
ISBN 0-948444-46-0